CONTENTS

CHARACTER LIST

NARRATOR(S)	A fairly big speaking part and would suit a child with a strong, clear speaking voice, or it could be split between two children.
SAM	One of two main characters; large speaking part.
THE SHREW	The other main character; large speaking part and would suit a child with a cheeky grin and a good sense of humour! Needs to dress as a shrew and could make a small mask to go across the eyes and nose. Alternatively, you could create a sock-puppet shrew to pop up from behind the hay bale. The large speaking part could then be split between two or more children and voiced accordingly.
CROWD	Have as many as you can for the crowd gathering in Bethlehem for the census.
INNKEEPER	Small speaking part.
JOSEPH	Small speaking part.
MARY	Small speaking part.
5 SHEPHERDS	Each has a short line to say.
3 WISE MEN	Each has a short line to say. Could perform some simple actions during Song 5 with brightly coloured, home-made telescopes.
GABRIEL	Small speaking part.
5 ANGELS	Each has a short line to say.
EXTRA SHEPHERDS/ANGELS	Optional non-speaking parts.
CHOIR	Instead of extra shepherd and angel parts, you could create a choir dressed in cowboy hats and neckerchiefs to give that country feel!
DONKEY	Optional non-speaking part; simple clip-clop movements could be performed during Song 3. Alternatively, a hobbyhorse could be used.
JOLLY FIDDLER	Optional part; he could appear at the side of the stage during Song 1, tapping his toes and pretending to play.
BABY JESUS	Don't forget the essential doll!

A note on stage directions

Suggested stage directions are provided throughout the script, but please note that these are meant as guidelines only. If you can't find real hay bales, cover large boxes with shredded yellow paper, or paint them yellow with brown flecks. If you are making a sock-puppet shrew, more farmyard-animal sock puppets could be made to feature in songs 2, 7 & 8.

SCRIPT

The stable scene is set towards the back of the stage, with at least two hay bales at one side, surrounded by brushes, shovels, buckets and any other stable equipment you can find, and the manger on the other. Loose hay should be scattered over the stable floor.

NARRATOR Many years ago, there lived a young stable boy called Sam. He worked cleaning the stables in the town of Bethlehem.

Enter Sam, sweeping the floor and looking sad.

THE SHREW *(Popping up from behind a hay bale)* Boo! Chin up, Sam, my old friend.

SAM *(Jumping back in surprise)* Shrew! You made me jump!

THE SHREW Sorry mate. I was trying to make you laugh. You look so sad.

SAM I am sad. Nobody ever notices my hard work cleaning this smelly stable.

THE SHREW The animals notice.

SAM Maybe, but I wish I had an important job.

THE SHREW You do have an important job, Sam. Come on – I think we need a song to cheer you up!

Song 1. THE STABLE HOEDOWN **CD track 1/9**

A small group could perform a simple line dance during Song 1, and a jolly fiddler could appear at the side of the stage, tapping his toes.

SAM *(Laughing)* Oh Shrew, I feel much better now, but I need a rest after all that singing!

Sam wipes his brow and sits on some hay. He jumps back up and runs around holding his bottom.

SAM Ow, ow, ow. That hay is prickly. My poor bottom!

THE SHREW Never mind your bottom, Sam. What about the poor animals? How do they sleep on this prickly hay?

SAM I don't know. I'd better go and get some new soft hay for them.

THE SHREW Can I help? Pleeeeeeease?

SAM Okey-dokey! You sweep out the old hay and I'll bring in the new.

Song 2. WORKING IN A STABLE **CD track 2/10**

NARRATOR Meanwhile, outside the stable, the streets were crowded. All the people in the land were gathering in Bethlehem for the census. This meant that they all had to be counted.

A bustling, noisy crowd, including Mary, Joseph and the donkey, crosses front of stage.

NARRATOR Joseph and his wife Mary were among those who had arrived in Bethlehem. Mary rode a donkey. She was expecting a baby. Joseph tried to find them a safe place to stay.

The innkeeper enters front stage left, holding a clipboard and pen. Mary and Joseph enter front stage right and cross to meet the innkeeper.

JOSEPH Excuse me Innkeeper, is there any room at the inn? We've tried so many already.

INNKEEPER *(Checking the clipboard)* No, I'm sorry, the last room has just gone.

MARY Oh dear. What are we going to do, Joseph?

INNKEEPER Don't worry, I have a stable. You may stay there if you like.

JOSEPH Yes please. Where is it?

INNKEEPER Follow me. It's just along this rocky road.

The instrumental section of the following song is ideal for adding percussion. Smaller children may enjoy banging coconut shells together. If you are using a 'real' donkey, he could perform simple clip-clop movements throughout the song.

Song 3. CLIP-CLOP LITTLE DONKEY **CD track 3/11**

Mary, Joseph, the donkey and the innkeeper exit the stage. Sam enters from the back of the stage with a pile of hay.

SAM Here we go. Lots of new soft hay for the animals. *(Looks around)* What did you do with the prickly hay, Shrew?

THE SHREW I put it in the manger.

SAM Oh yes, what a good idea! (*A clip-clop sound is heard and Sam and Shrew stop to listen)* What's that clip-clop sound?

THE SHREW *(Clip-clop sound continues)* It's getting closer.

SAM Quick, hide! There's somebody coming into the stable! *(Sam and Shrew hide behind a hay bale)*

Mary, Joseph, the donkey and the innkeeper enter from the back of the stage.

INNKEEPER Here we are at the stable.

JOSEPH Thank you.

INNKEEPER Goodnight.

MARY & JOSEPH Goodnight.

The innkeeper exits at the back of the stage.

NARRATOR That night, Mary's baby was born in the stable. She named Him Jesus and laid Him in the manger.

Mary places the baby in the manger and Joseph stands next to her. Meanwhile, Shrew pops up from behind the hay bale, unseen by Mary and Joseph.

THE SHREW *(Looking down at Sam)* Sam, Sam, wake up! You won't believe this!

SAM *(Popping up from behind the hay bale)* What is it, Shrew?

THE SHREW There's a baby in the manger!

SAM *(Shocked)* Whoa! *(The baby starts to cry)*

SFX: Crying Baby Jesus **CD track 17**

MARY Oh Joseph, the baby can't sleep. What shall we do?

JOSEPH Let's take him out to look at that beautiful bright star.

Mary and Joseph exit at the back of the stage with the baby.

THE SHREW No wonder the baby can't sleep in that manger. It's full of prickly hay!

SAM Well, why don't we swap the prickly hay for some new soft hay to make it comfortable for the baby?

THE SHREW Good idea, Sam. Do it quickly, before they get back!

Sam swaps the hay and returns to hide behind the hay bale with Shrew. Mary and Joseph re-enter at the back of the stage with the baby. Mary places him in the manger.

MARY Oh Joseph, this hay is so soft.

Sam and Shrew pop up from behind the hay bale with a 'thumbs up' signal, then they bob back down to hide.

NARRATOR Mary sang a lullaby to her baby as He went off to sleep peacefully in the soft, comfortable hay.

SONG 4. MARY'S LULLABY **CD track 4/12**

JOSEPH *(A knocking sound is heard)* Who is it?

The shepherds enter from the back of the stage with their crooks.

SHEPHERD 1 We are poor shepherds.

SHEPHERD 2 We were minding our sheep when God's angels appeared to us.

SHEPHERD 3 They said, 'Do not be afraid, we bring good news!'

SHEPHERD 4 And then they told us to come here.

SHEPHERD 5 Because an important baby has been born.

MARY That's right, and His name is Jesus.

The shepherds kneel beside the manger. A knocking sound is heard again. The innkeeper enters from the back of the stage.

INNKEEPER Excuse me, there are some more people here to see your baby. They look very posh!

The innkeeper stays on stage and the Three Wise Men enter with gifts wrapped in shiny paper.

CASPAR We are wise men from the east.

MELCHIOR We have been following a bright star.

BALTHAZAR We have come to worship the newborn King.

JOSEPH Welcome. Please tell us more!

The Three Wise Men could perform an action dance during the following song, pointing colourful telescopes to the left, to the right, up, down and all around.

Song 5. THREE WISE MEN **CD track 5/13**

The Three Wise Men lay their gifts at the foot of the manger. Sam and Shrew peep out from behind the hay bale.

CASPAR My name is Caspar. I bring gold.

MELCHIOR My name is Melchior. I bring frankincense.

BALTHAZAR My name is Balthazar. I bring myrrh.

The angels enter and everyone looks startled!

GABRIEL Do not be afraid.

ANGEL 1 A King is born today.

ANGEL 2 Let's celebrate!

Sam jumps up, cheering. Everyone looks at him and he stops abruptly.

INNKEEPER Stable boy! What are you doing here? You don't belong with these important people.

GABRIEL But wait! *(Turns to Sam)* Are you the boy who made this stable so clean and cosy?

SAM Yes, with the help of my friend the shrew. *(Shrew rises slowly from behind the hay bale)*

ANGEL 3 Well, what an important job!

ANGEL 4 Do you know that God sees all of your hard work?

ANGEL 5 He is very proud of you, even when nobody else notices.

Song 6. IF YOU THINK YOU'RE NOT IMPORTANT **CD track 6/14**

The entire cast remains on stage.

THE SHREW I always told you that you were important, Sam.

SAM And so are you, Shrew!

THE SHREW But we only did a little job moving the hay.

SAM A little job, but a very important job.

SAM & THE SHREW Hooray for prickly hay! *(Sam and Shrew hug each other)*

Song 7. PRICKLY HAY **CD track 7/15**

NARRATOR The birth of Jesus made everyone in the stable feel important that night.

GABRIEL Let's all remember how important we are, because Jesus came for everyone.

SAM So, what are we going to do?

ALL Party!

Song 8. CHRISTMAS IS FOR YOU **CD track 8/16**

The Stable Hoedown

Words and Music by
Kelly Fort

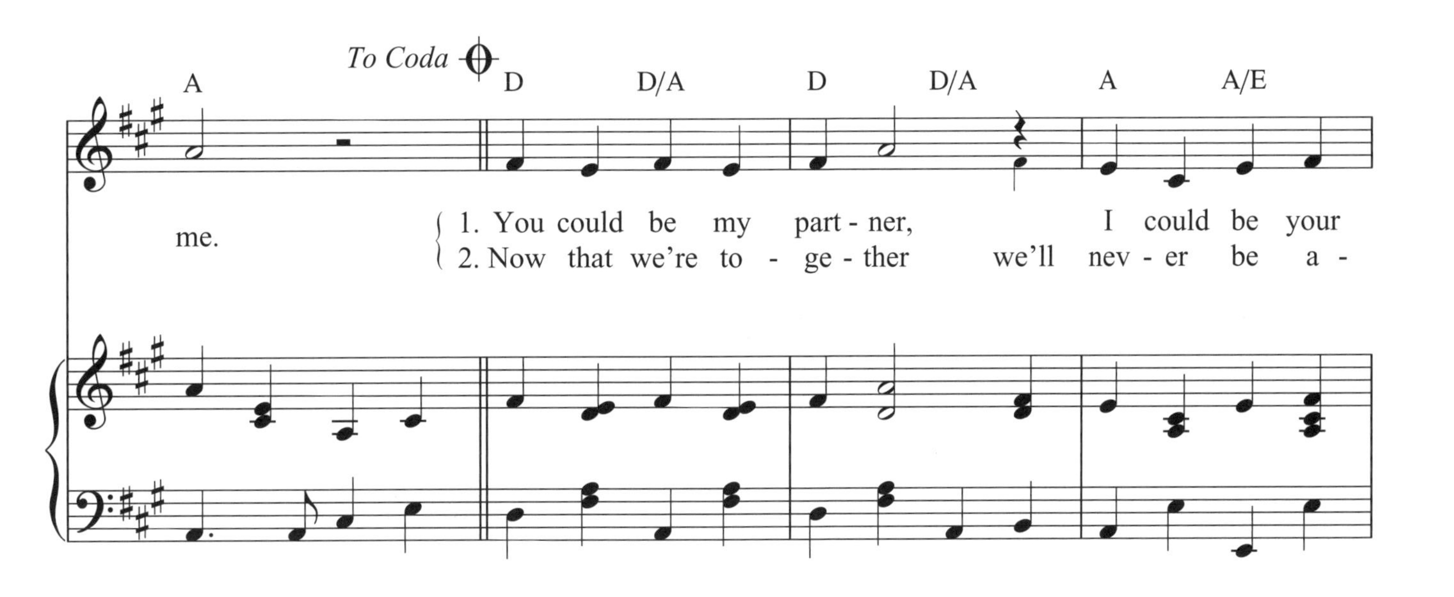
To Coda
A
D
D/A
D
D/A
A
A/E
me.
1. You could be my part - ner, I could be your
2. Now that we're to - ge - ther we'll nev - er be a -

A
B7
B7/F♯
B7
B7/F♯
friend, we'll dance all day 'til the sun goes down, the
- lone, we'll dance all day 'til the sun goes down, we'll

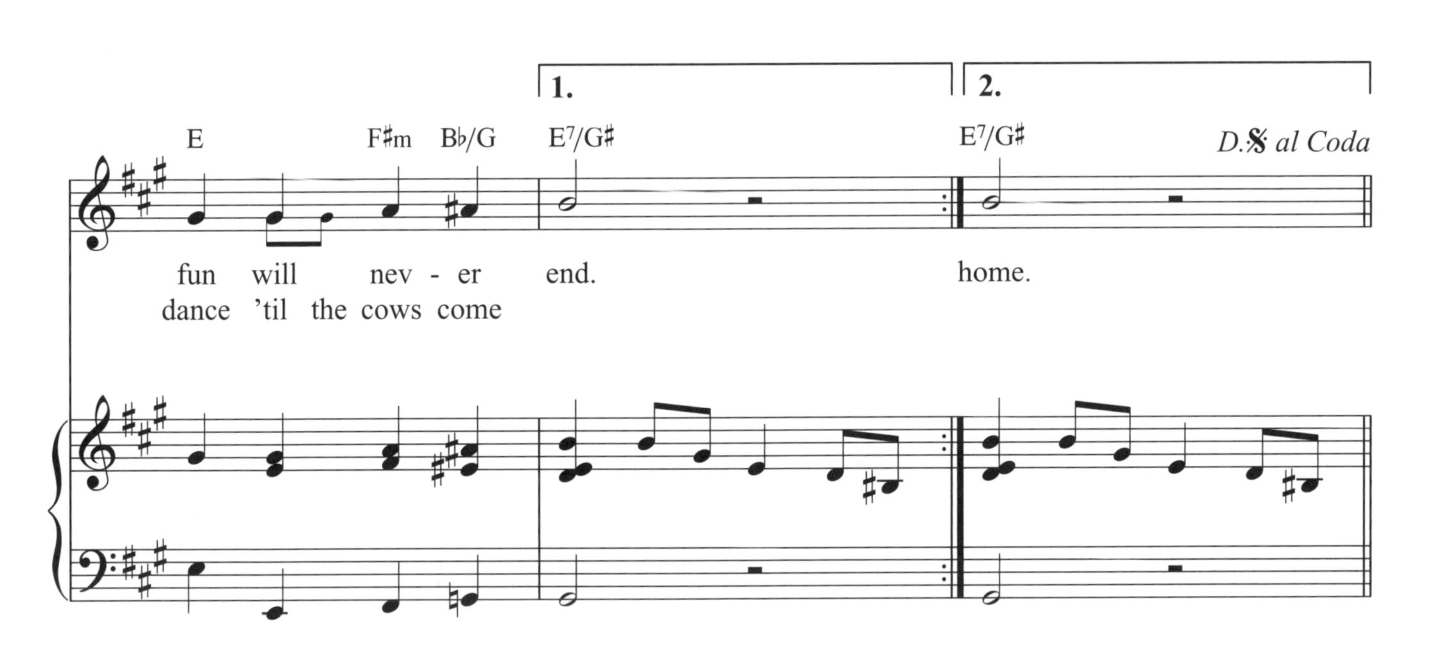
1.
2.
E
F♯m
B♭/G
E7/G♯
E7/G♯
D.S. al Coda
fun will nev - er end.
dance 'til the cows come
home.

CODA
A A/C♯ D D/F♯ A A/C♯ D D/F♯ D/A
Instrumental

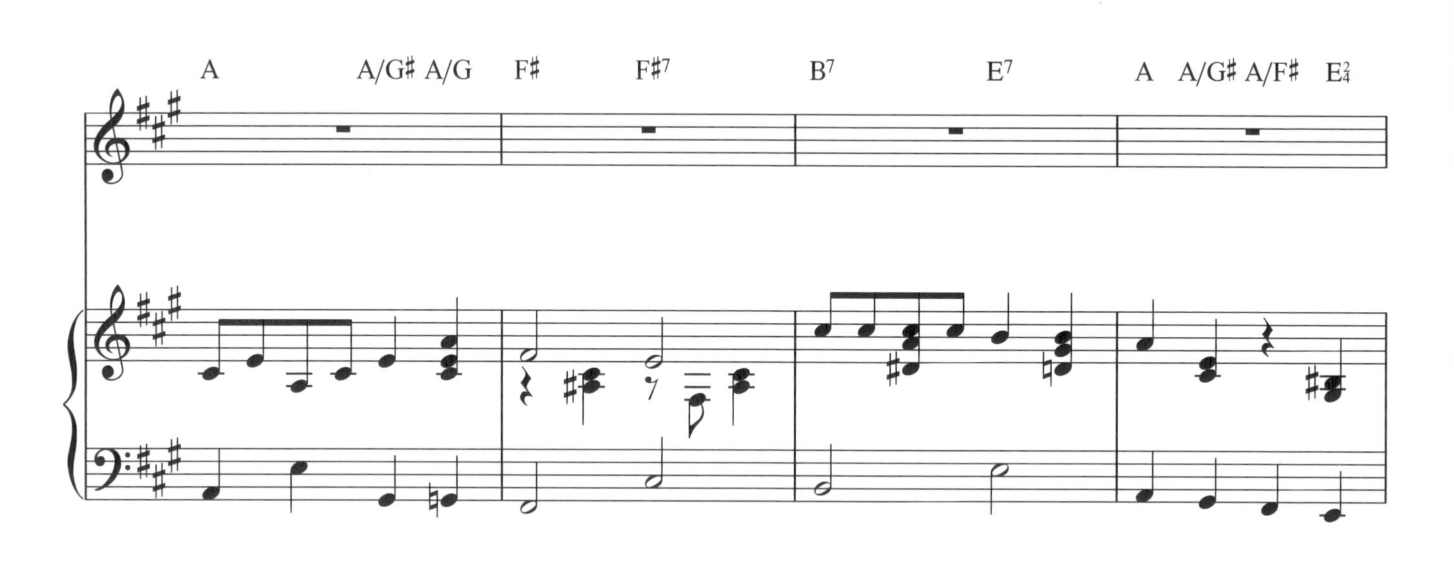
A A/G♯ A/G F♯ F♯7 B7 E7 A A/G♯ A/F♯ E$^{2}_{4}$

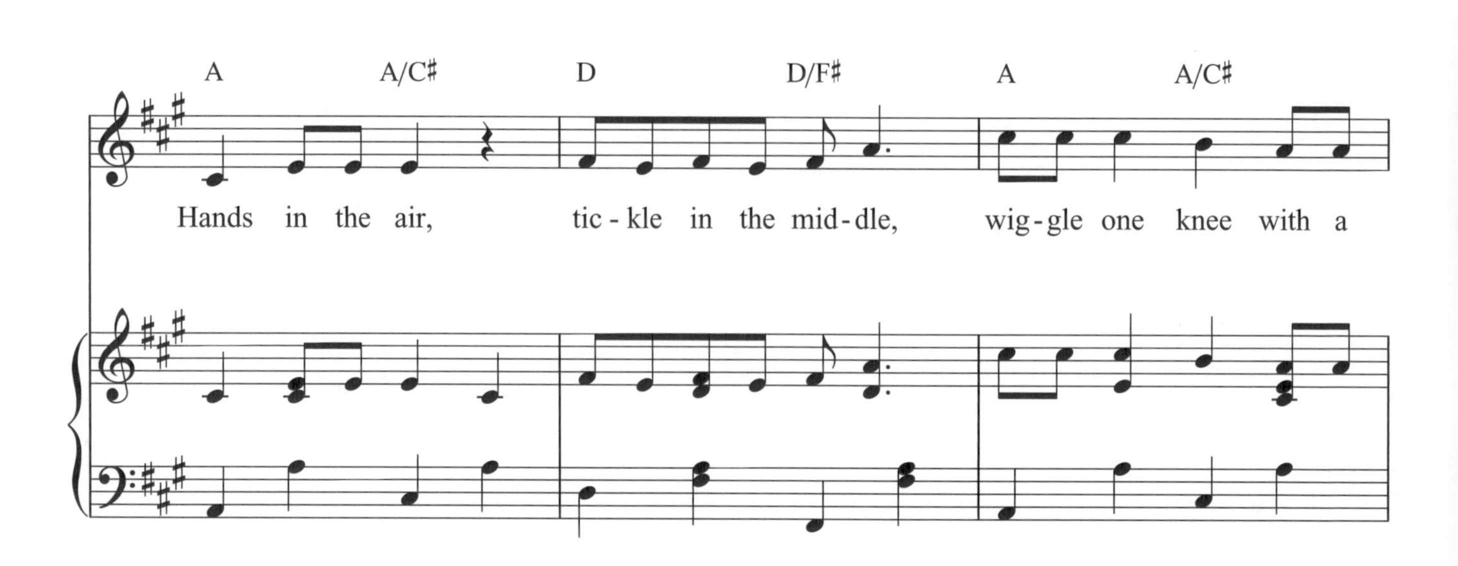
A A/C♯ D D/F♯ A A/C♯
Hands in the air, tic-kle in the mid-dle, wig-gle one knee with a

D
D/F♯
D/A
A
A/G♯
A/G
F♯
F♯7
one, two, three, we're do - ing the sta - ble hoe - down,

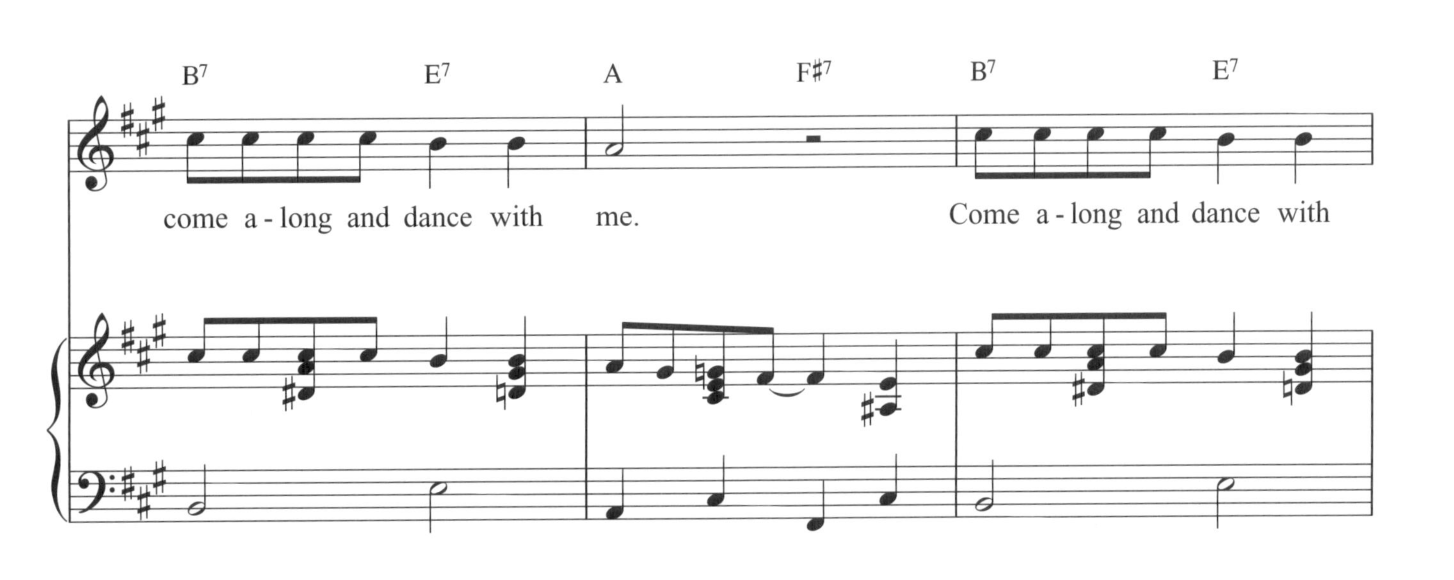
B7
E7
A
F♯7
B7
E7
come a - long and dance with me. Come a - long and dance with

A
F♯7
B7
E7
A
G♯6
A6
me. Come a - long and dance with me. YEE - HA!

Working In A Stable

Words and Music by
Kelly Fort

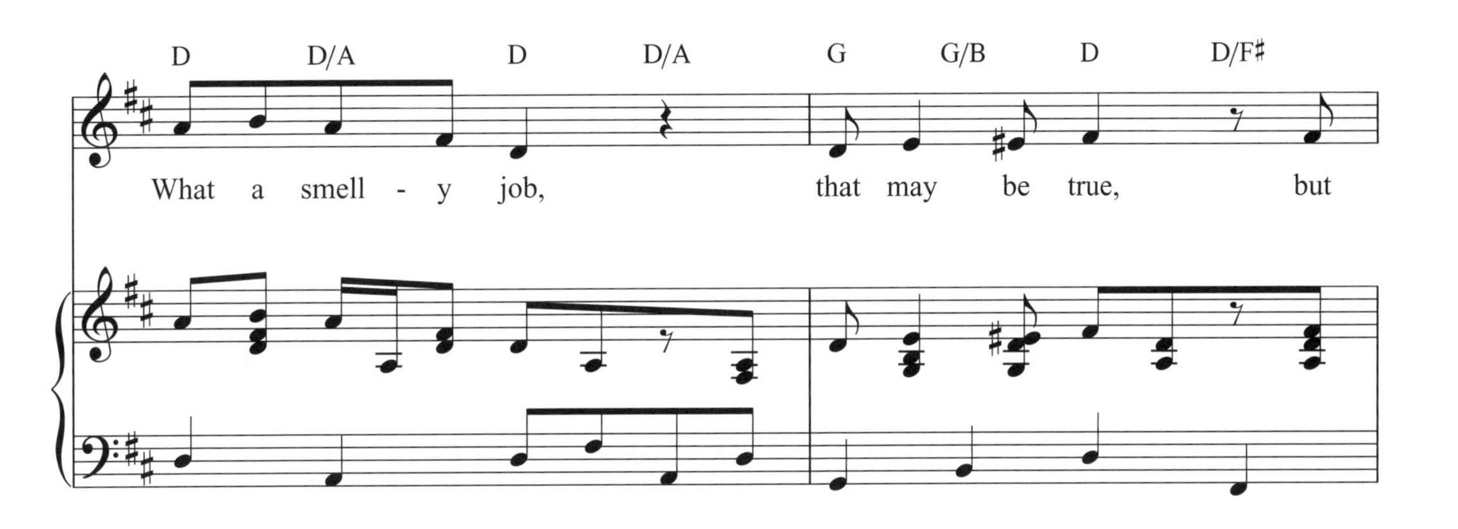
D D/A D D/A G G/B D D/F♯
What a smell - y job, that may be true, but

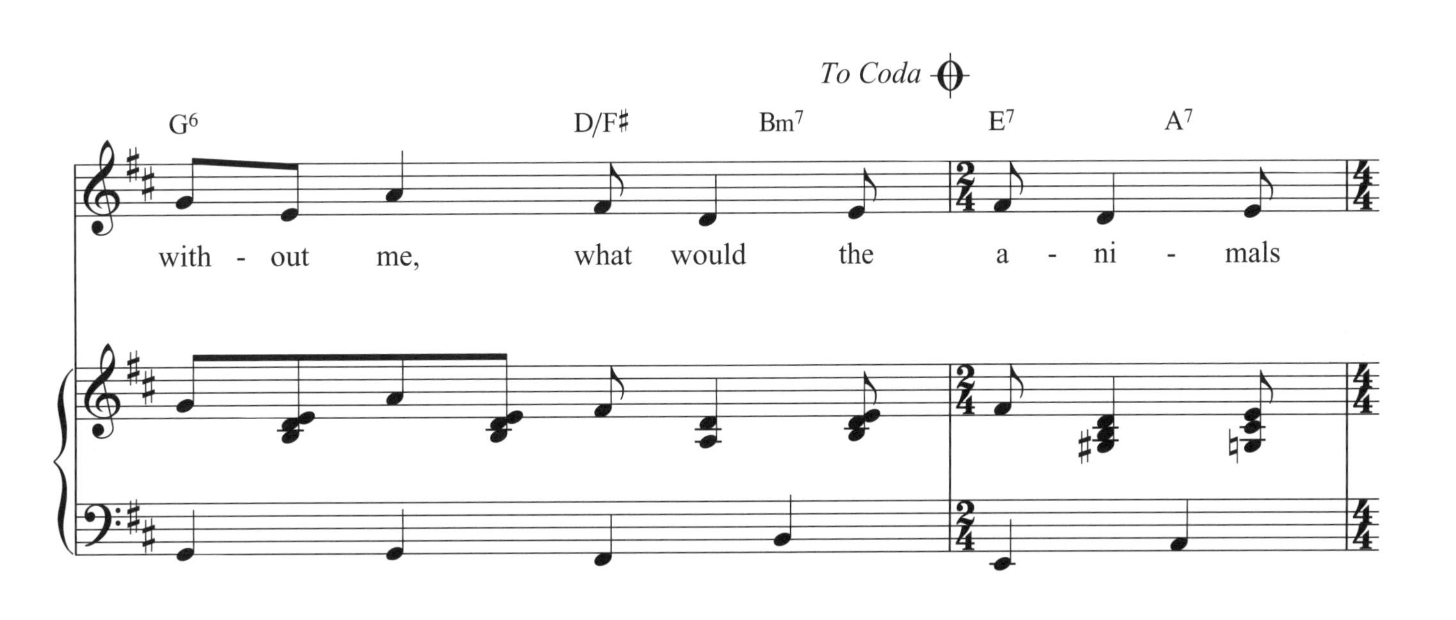
To Coda
G6 D/F♯ Bm7 E7 A7
with - out me, what would the a - ni - mals

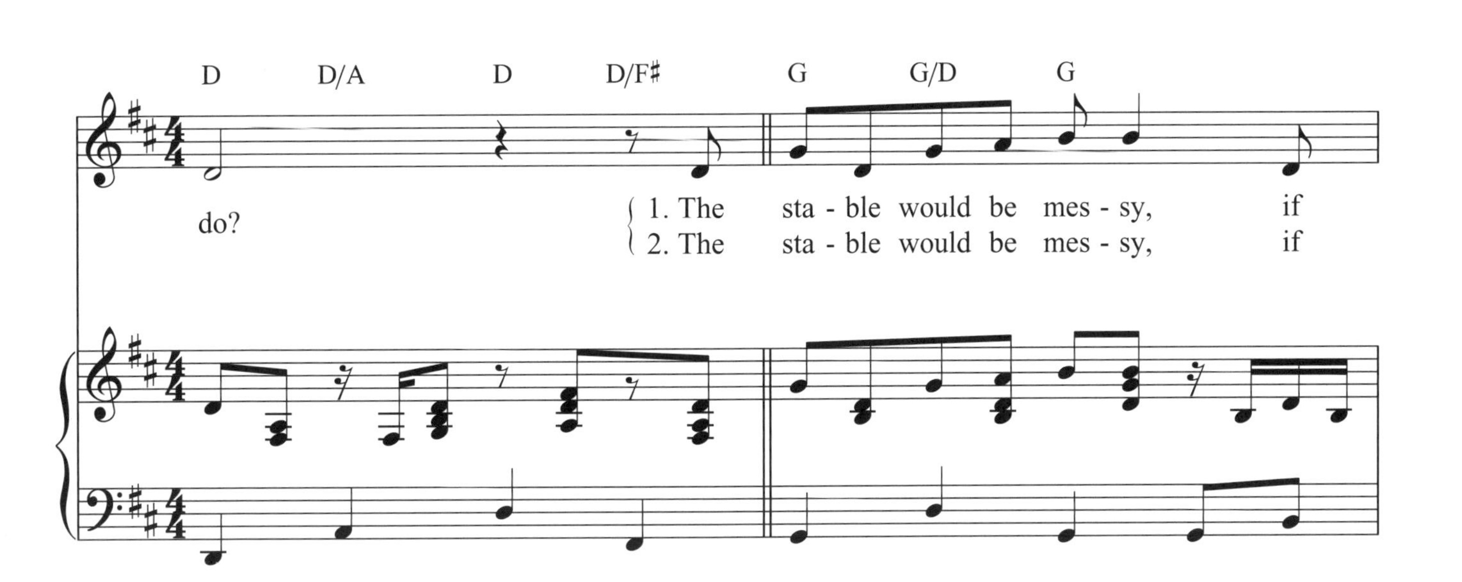
D D/A D D/F♯ G G/D G
do? 1. The sta - ble would be mes - sy, if
2. The sta - ble would be mes - sy, if

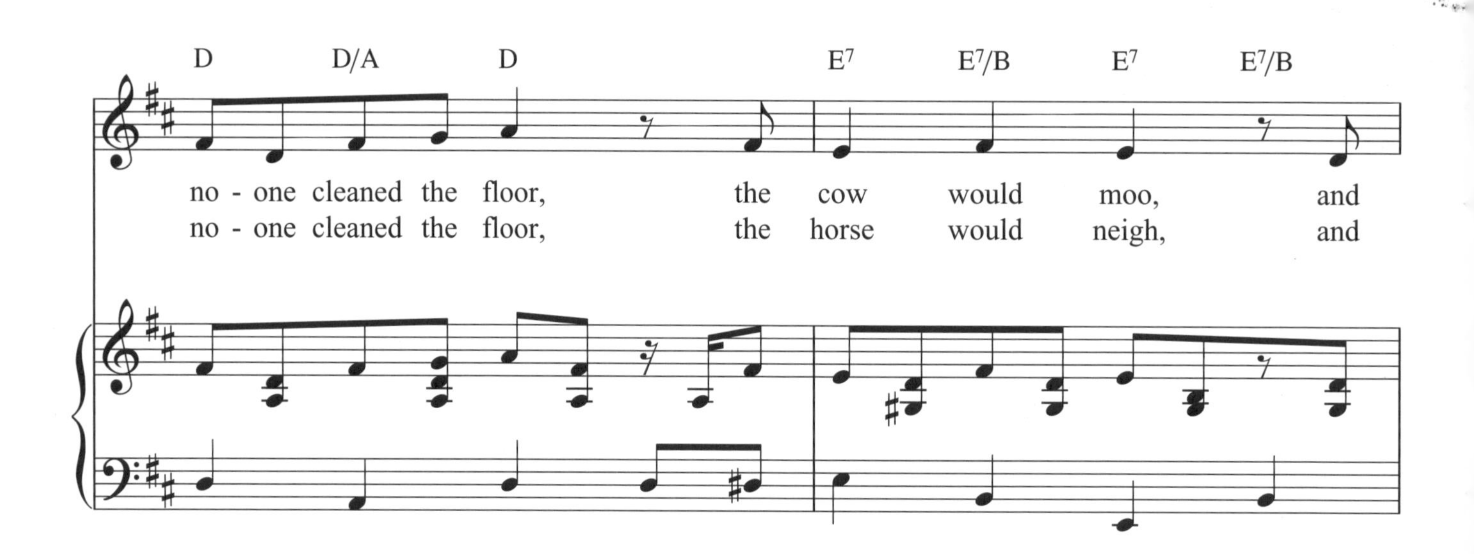
D D/A D E7 E7/B E7 E7/B
no - one cleaned the floor, the cow would moo, and
no - one cleaned the floor, the horse would neigh, and

A Bm7 A7/C♯ D D/A D D/A
moo some more. Moo, moo, moo, moo, moo,
neigh some more. Neigh, neigh, neigh, neigh, neigh,

G G/B D D/F♯ G G/B D Bm7
moo, moo, moo, moo. Moo, moo, moo, moo, moo,
neigh, neigh, neigh, neigh. Neigh, neigh, neigh, neigh, neigh,

1.
E7 A7 D D/A D A Bm7 A7/C♯
moo, moo, moo, moo.
neigh, neigh, neigh,

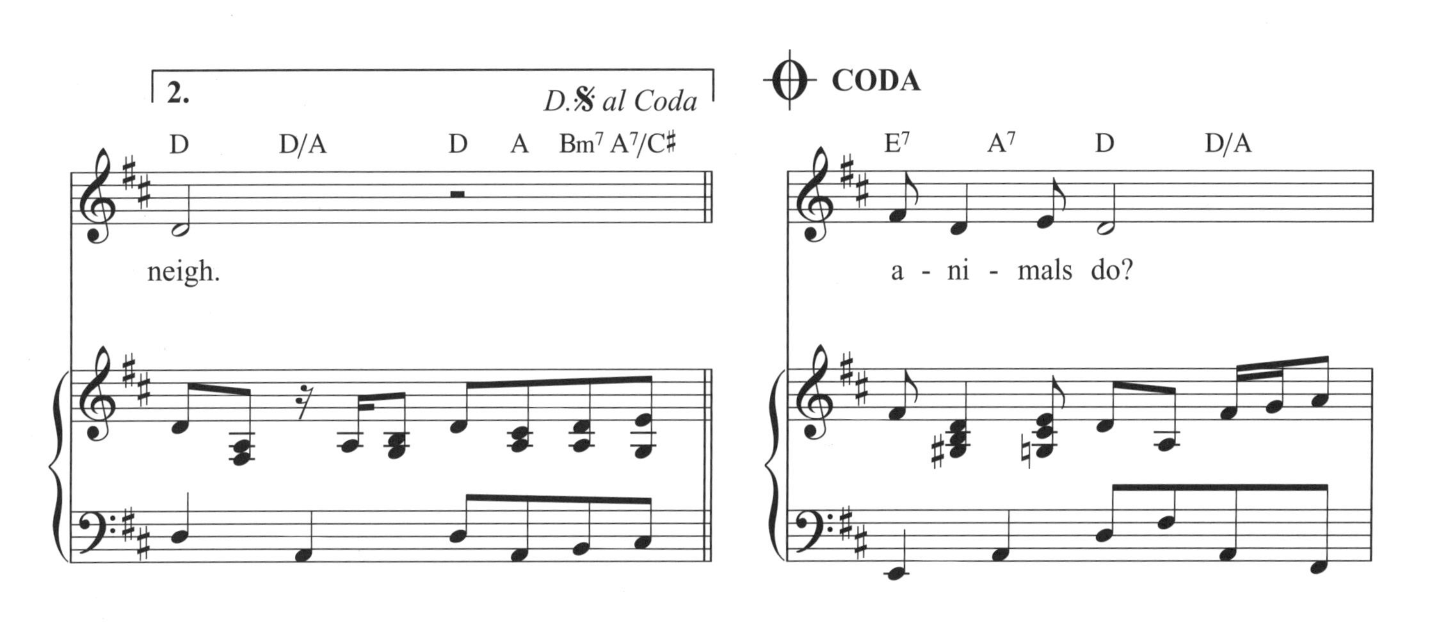
2.
D.𝄋 al Coda
CODA
D D/A D A Bm7 A7/C♯
neigh.
E7 A7 D D/A
a - ni - mals do?

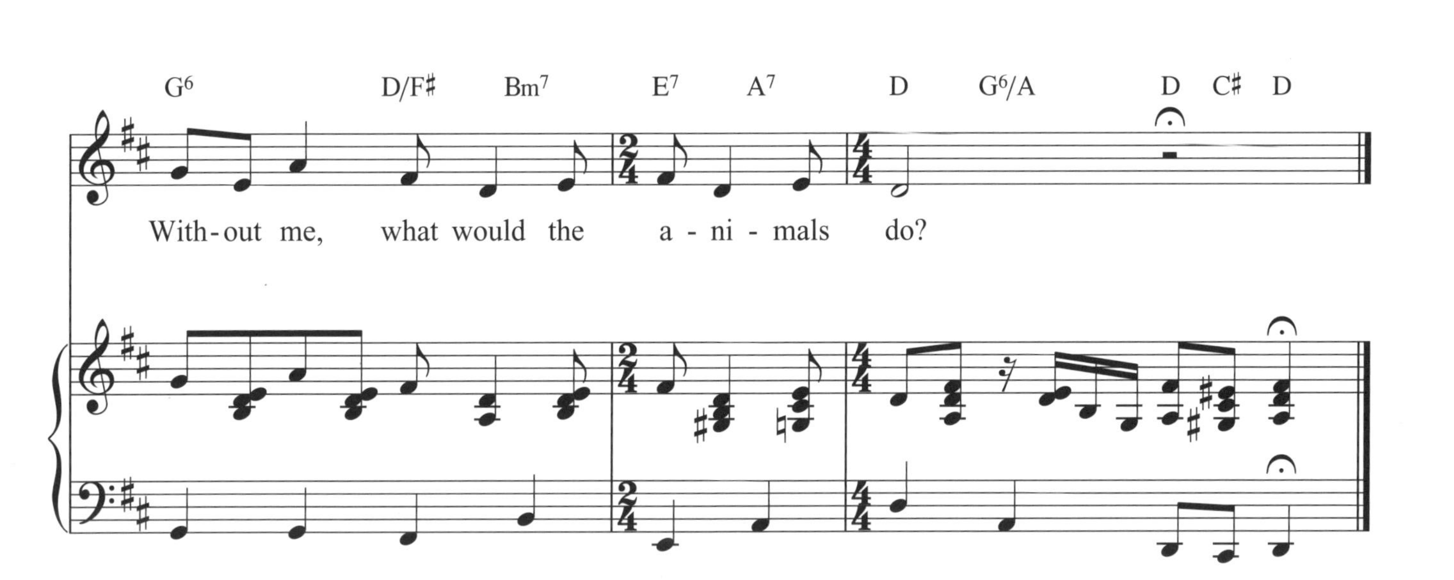
G6 D/F♯ Bm7 E7 A7 D G6/A D C♯ D
With-out me, what would the a - ni - mals do?

Clip-Clop Little Donkey

Words and Music by
Kelly Fort

1.
2.
Gm
D7
D9
Gm
C/D
Clip-clop lit-tle don-key,
Clip-clop lit-tle don-key,
on the rock-y road.
D9
Gm
Cm7
stead-y with your load.
Jo-seph lead the way for us.
N.C.
Cm7
Gm7
Cm7
Clip-clop. Clip-clop.
Find a place to stay for us.
Am7
D7(#9)
Gm
Clip-clop. Don't stop!
3. Clip-clop lit-tle don-key,

Gm/C
Dm7(♭5)
D9
can you car-ry Ma - ry?
Gm
Clip-clop lit-tle don - key,
D7
D9
Gm
C/D
on the rock-y road.
Gm
Instrumental
Gm Gm(maj7)/D
Gm7
Gm6/D
Gm Gm(maj7)/D
Gm7
Gm6/D
Cm7
Jo - seph lead the way for us.

N.C.
Cm7
Gm7
Cm7
Clip-clop. Clip-clop. Find a place to stay_ for us._
Am7
D7(♯9)
Gm
Clip-clop. Don't stop!
4. Clip-clop lit-tle don-key,
5. Clip-clop lit-tle don-key, she's
Gm/C
Dm7(♭5)
D9
Gm
can you car-ry Ma-ry? Clip-clop lit-tle don-key,
gon-na have a ba-by. Clip-clop lit-tle don-key,
1.
2.
D9
Gm
C/D
D9
Gm
on the rock-y road.
stead-y with_ your load.

Mary's Lullaby

Words and Music by
Kelly Fort

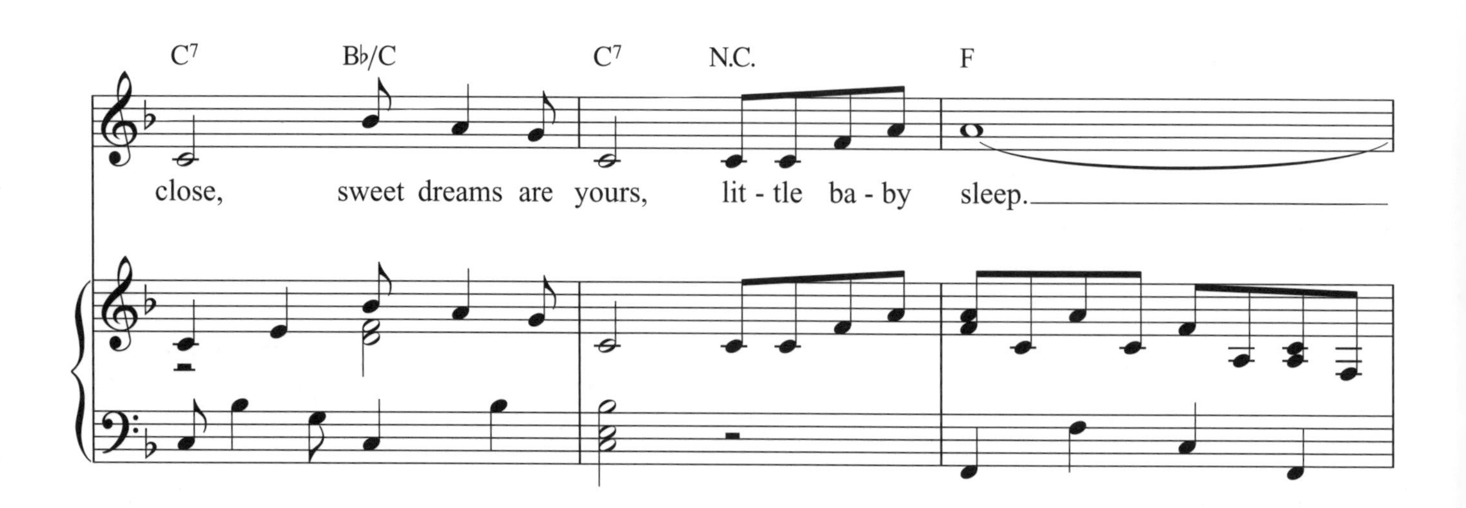

C7
N.C.
F
2. Lit - tle ba - by rest,
God is watch-ing

B♭
C7
B♭/C
o - ver you,
hear - ing my prayer,
safe in his

C7
F
B♭/F
F
care, lit - tle ba - by rest.

B♭
F
C7
Sleep, sleep, sleep lit - tle ba - by
F
B♭
F
sleep. Sleep, sleep,
C7
F
sleep lit - tle ba - by sleep.
Instrumental
B♭

C7
B♭/C
C7
F
C7
B♭
F
Sleep,
sleep,
C7
F
F/A
B♭
sleep lit - tle ba - by sleep.
Sleep,
F
C7
F
sleep,
sleep lit - tle ba - by sleep.

Three Wise Men

Words and Music by
Kelly Fort

Steadily ♩ = 82
Bm

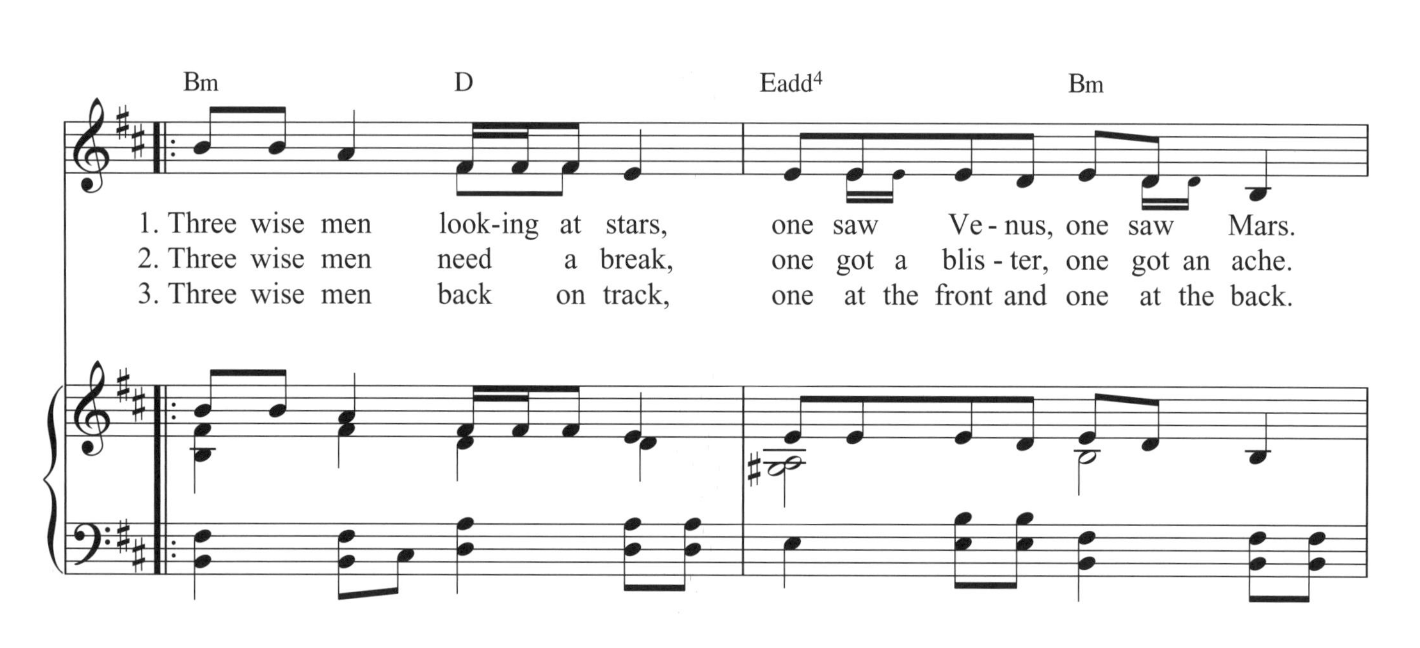
Bm
D
Eadd4
Bm
1. Three wise men looking at stars, one saw Ve - nus, one saw Mars.
2. Three wise men need a break, one got a blis - ter, one got an ache.
3. Three wise men back on track, one at the front and one at the back.

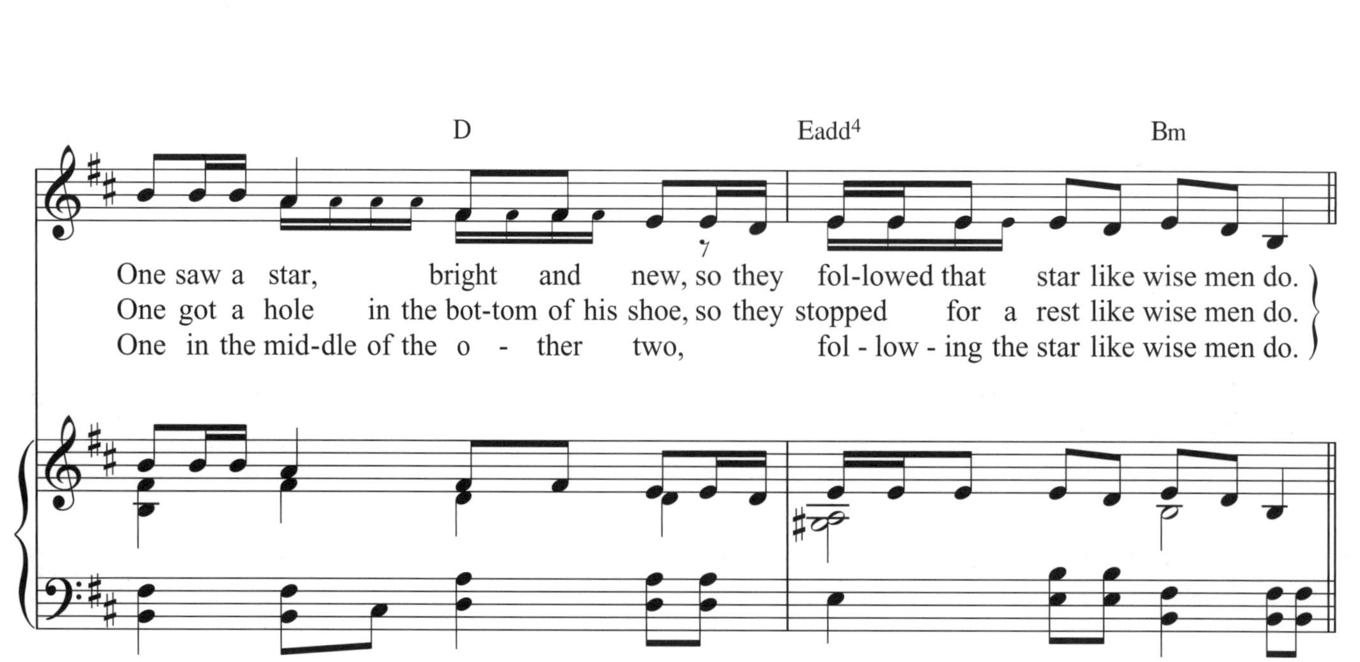
D
Eadd4
Bm
One saw a star, bright and new, so they fol-lowed that star like wise men do.
One got a hole in the bot-tom of his shoe, so they stopped for a rest like wise men do.
One in the mid-dle of the o - ther two, fol - low - ing the star like wise men do.

Eadd4
Bm
Fol-low it to the left,
fol-low it to the right,
D
F♯5
E5
D5
B5
up, down, all a - round,
shi - ning, shi - ning bright.
1. 2.
A5
B5
A5
E5
F♯5
E5
D5
Bm
3.
F♯5
E5
D5
Bm
Fol-low that star to - night.

If You Think You're Not Important

Words and Music by
Kelly Fort

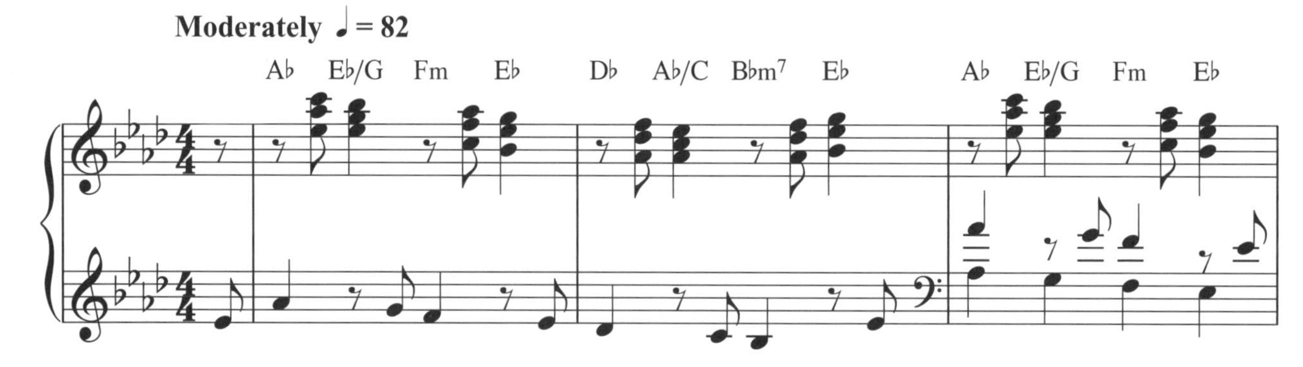

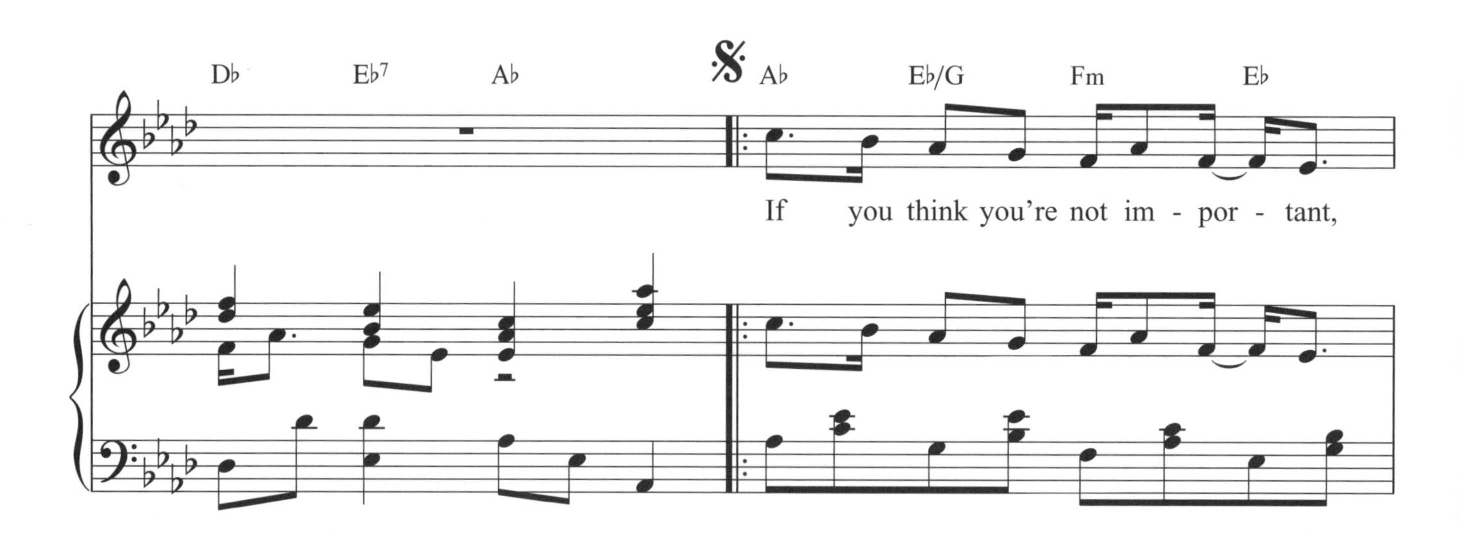

B♭m/D♭ E♭7 A♭
ve-ry proud of you!
D♭ D♭/A♭ D♭ D♭/A♭
1. Think a-bout the sta-ble boy,
2. Think a-bout the shep-herds,
3. Think of ba-by Je-sus,
A♭/C A♭ A♭/C A♭ B♭7 B♭7/F B♭ B♭/D
work-ing ev-ery day. He had an im-por-tant job
on the hill-side steep. They had an im-por-tant job
sent from God a-bove. He had an im-por-tant job
1. 2.
E♭7 E♭7/G
sort-ing out the hay!
look-ing af-ter sheep!
3.
D.𝄋 al Coda
E♭7 E♭7/G
bring-ing peace and love!
CODA
B♭m/D♭ E♭7 A♭ B♭m7 A♭/C
ve-ry proud of you! He's
D♭ E♭7 A♭ E♭/G Fm E♭ D♭ E♭7 A♭ G A♭
ve-ry proud of you!

Prickly Hay

Words and Music by
Kelly Fort

To Coda
F F/A F/C B♭ B♭/D B♭/F E♭
in some pric - k - ly hay.
1. The lit - tle ba - by Je -
2. Shep-herds went to see
3. Three wise men went search -
B♭ E♭ B♭ E♭
- sus, did - n't have a bed, so they laid Him in some
Him, in that cat - tle shed, and there He lay in the
- ing, gui - ded by a star, I can't re - mem - ber
1. 2.
B♭ G7 C7 F F/E♭ F/D F7/C
pric - k - ly hay, in a cat - tle shed.
pric - k - ly hay, just like the an - gel said.
two of their names, but

3.
C7
F
E♭/F
one was called Bal - tha - zar,
Bal - tha - zar,
D.𝄋 al Coda
F7
F7/E♭ F7/D F7/C
Bal - tha - zar!
CODA
B♭ B♭/D B♭/F B♭ B♭/D B♭/F E♭ E♭/G E♭/B♭
Instrumental
F F/A F/C B♭ B♭/D E♭/F B♭ B♭/D B♭/F

E♭ E♭/G E♭/B♭ F F/A F/C B♭ B♭/D E♭/F
B♭ B♭/D B♭/F E♭ E♭/G E♭/B♭
Pric - k - ly hay, pric - k - ly hay, they
F F/A F/C B♭ B♭/D E♭/F B♭ B♭/D B♭/F
laid Him in some pric - k - ly hay, in a man - ger,
E♭ E♭/G E♭/B♭ F F/A F/C B♭ A6 B♭6
far a - way, in some pric - k - ly hay.

Christmas Is For You

Words and Music by
Kelly Fort

With energy ♩ = 176

D D/F♯ D/A G G/B G/D D D/F♯ D/A
1. Christ - mas is for me, (clap, clap) Christ - mas is for you,
2. Christ - mas is for rich, (clap, clap) Christ - mas is for poor,
3. Christ - mas is for girls, (clap, clap) Christ - mas is for boys,
A A/C♯ A/E D D/F♯ D/A G G/B G/D D A7
(clap, clap) Je - sus came for ev - ery - one so what are we gon - na
(clap, clap) Je - sus came for ev - ery - one so what are we wait - ing
(clap, clap) Je - sus came for ev - ery - one so why don't we make some
D D/F♯ D/A G G/B G/D G G/B G/D
do?
for?
noise?
We're gon - na hold a par - ty,

D G/D G/A D D/F♯ D/A Bm7
dance the whole night through. Don't miss out on
Bm/A E7 To Coda 1. 2. A A7 3. A A7
ce - le - bra - ting, Christ-mas is for you! you!
D
Instrumental
D.𝄋 al Coda
D7/A D7/F♯

CODA
A G G/B G/D G G/B G/D
you! We're gon - na hold a par - ty,
D G/D G/A D D/F♯ D/A Bm7
dance the whole night through. Don't miss out on
Em9 E7 G/A A7
ce - le - bra - ting, Christ - mas is for
D D/F♯ D/A G G/B G/D D G/A D
you!

The Stable Hoedown

CHORUS *Hands in the air,*
Tickle in the middle,
Wiggle one knee with a 1, 2, 3,
We're doing the stable hoedown,
Come along and dance with me.

1 You could be my partner,
I could be your friend,
We'll dance all day 'til the sun goes down,
The fun will never end.

CHORUS

2 Now that we're together
We'll never be alone,
We'll dance all day 'til the sun goes down,
We'll dance 'til the cows come home.

CHORUS

Instrumental (for line dancing)

CHORUS *Hands in the air,*
Tickle in the middle,
Wiggle one knee with a 1, 2, 3,
We're doing the stable hoedown,
Come along and dance with me.
Come along and dance with me.
Come along and dance with me.
YEE-HA!

Words and Music by Kelly Fort

CCLI Song No. 5953697

Working In A Stable

CHORUS *Working in a stable, this is what I do,*
Sweep out the old hay, bring in the new.
What a smelly job, that may be true,
But without me, what would the animals do?

1 The stable would be messy,
If no-one cleaned the floor,
The cow would moo, and moo some more.
Moo, moo, moo, moo, moo,
Moo, moo, moo, moo.
Moo, moo, moo, moo, moo,
Moo, moo, moo, moo.

CHORUS

2 The stable would be messy,
If no-one cleaned the floor,
The horse would neigh, and neigh some more.
Neigh, neigh, neigh, neigh, neigh,
Neigh, neigh, neigh, neigh.
Neigh, neigh, neigh, neigh, neigh,
Neigh, neigh, neigh, neigh.

CHORUS *Working in a stable, this is what I do,*
Sweep out the old hay, bring in the new.
What a smelly job, that may be true,
But without me, what would the animals do?
Without me, what would the animals do?

Words and Music by Kelly Fort

CCLI Song No. 5953714

Clip-Clop Little Donkey

1 Clip-clop little donkey,
Can you carry Mary?
Clip-clop little donkey,
On the rocky road.

2 Clip-clop little donkey,
She's gonna have a baby.
Clip-clop little donkey,
Steady with your load.

BRIDGE *Joseph lead the way for us.*
Clip-clop. Clip-clop.
Find a place to stay for us.
Clip-clop. Don't stop!

3 Clip-clop little donkey,
Can you carry Mary?
Clip-clop little donkey,
On the rocky road.

Instrumental

BRIDGE

4 Clip-clop little donkey,
Can you carry Mary?
Clip-clop little donkey,
On the rocky road.

5 Clip-clop little donkey,
She's gonna have a baby.
Clip-clop little donkey,
Steady with your load.

Words and Music by Kelly Fort

CCLI Song No. 5953738

Mary's Lullaby

1 Little baby sleep,
For you've had a busy day.
Little eyes close,
Sweet dreams are yours,
Little baby sleep.

2 Little baby rest,
God is watching over you,
Hearing my prayer,
Safe in his care,
Little baby rest.

CHORUS *Sleep, sleep,*
Sleep little baby sleep.
Sleep, sleep,
Sleep little baby sleep.

Instrumental

CHORUS (with harmonies)
Sleep, sleep,
Sleep little baby sleep.
Sleep, sleep,
Sleep little baby sleep.

Words and Music by Kelly Fort

CCLI Song No. 5953745

Three Wise Men

1 Three wise men looking at stars,
One saw Venus, one saw Mars.
One saw a star, bright and new,
So they followed that star like wise men do.

CHORUS *Follow it to the left,*
Follow it to the right,
Up, down, all around,
Shining, shining bright.

2 Three wise men need a break,
One got a blister, one got an ache.
One got a hole in the bottom of his shoe,
So they stopped for a rest like wise men do.

CHORUS

3 Three wise men back on track,
One at the front and one at the back.
One in the middle of the other two,
Following the star like wise men do.

CHORUS *Follow it to the left,*
Follow it to the right,
Up, down, all around,
Shining, shining bright.
Follow that star tonight.

Words and Music by Kelly Fort

CCLI Song No. 5953752

If You Think You're Not Important

CHORUS *If you think you're not important,*
For the little things you do,
Just remember God above
Is very proud of you!

1 Think about the stable boy,
Working every day.
He had an important job
Sorting out the hay!

CHORUS

2 Think about the shepherds,
On the hillside steep.
They had an important job
Looking after sheep!

CHORUS

3 Think of baby Jesus,
Sent from God above.
He had an important job
Bringing peace and love!

CHORUS *If you think you're not important,*
For the little things you do,
Just remember God above
Is very proud of you!
He's very proud of you!

Words and Music by Kelly Fort

CCLI Song No. 5953769

Prickly Hay

CHORUS *Prickly hay, prickly hay,*
They laid Him in some prickly hay,
In a manger, far away,
In some prickly hay.

1 The little baby Jesus,
Didn't have a bed,
So they laid Him in some prickly hay,
In a cattle shed.

CHORUS

2 Shepherds went to see Him,
In that cattle shed,
And there He lay in the prickly hay,
Just like the angel said.

CHORUS

3 Three wise men went searching,
Guided by a star,
I can't remember two of their names,
But one was called Balthazar,
Balthazar, Balthazar!

CHORUS

Instrumental

CHORUS

Words and Music by Kelly Fort

CCLI Song No. 5953790

Christmas Is For You

1 Christmas is for me, *(clap, clap)*
Christmas is for you, *(clap, clap)*
Jesus came for everyone
So what are we gonna do?

CHORUS *We're gonna hold a party,*
Dance the whole night through.
Don't miss out on celebrating,
Christmas is for you!

2 Christmas is for rich, *(clap, clap)*
Christmas is for poor, *(clap, clap)*
Jesus came for everyone
So what are we waiting for?

CHORUS

3 Christmas is for girls, *(clap, clap)*
Christmas is for boys, *(clap, clap)*
Jesus came for everyone
So why don't we make some noise?

CHORUS

Instrumental

CHORUS x 2

Words and Music by Kelly Fort

CCLI Song No. 5953800

COPYRIGHT & LICENSING - What You Need To Know

The world of copyright and licensing can seem very daunting, particularly because there is an obligation on schools to comply with copyright law. We're here to help you through the process and to keep you legal. The guidelines below explain the most common copyright and licensing issues.

Staging This Musical

Performing this musical to an audience (other than pupils and staff) requires a performance licence.

**** Please note that your Performing Rights Society (PRS) Licence does NOT cover musicals****

We issue affordable performance licences to schools, churches and nurseries. To apply, simply complete the performance licence application form on page 47 and fax or post it to us.

The performance licence will permit the holder to:

- Perform the musical on the dates applied for.
- Reproduce the song lyrics on printed paper, e.g. for programmes, to make transparencies for overhead projection and to display the lyrics on an interactive whiteboard or other type of screen. The following credit should be included with the lyrics:
  'Reproduced by kind permission © Out of the Ark Ltd'
- Photocopy the script for learning purposes. Copies must be destroyed after the performance.
- Make up to two photocopies of the music score for use by participating musicians on the performance dates.
- Play the CD (either backing tracks or vocal tracks) at the performance.

Putting On A Concert

If you are not staging this musical but are performing any of our songs for the public on school premises (i.e. to anyone other than pupils or staff) then royalty payments become due. Contact Out of the Ark Music directly to obtain a licence. **Please note:** There is no need to obtain a licence from the publisher if your school has an arrangement with the **Performing Rights Society (PRS)** either directly or through the local authority.

Making an Audio Recording or a Video of the Performance

If you wish to make an audio or video recording of your performance of any of our works please visit www.outoftheark.com/licensing for further information.

Singing Songs in the Classroom

You are free to use all of the material – including songs and scripts – in the classroom for teaching purposes. If photocopying any part of the book for teaching purposes please record this usage on your school's photocopy log to ensure that you are legally protected.

Singing Songs in an Assembly or in Church

Songs may be sung in assembly without charge. In addition the CD may be played provided that your school has a PRS licence. However, the reproduction of the lyrics and/or musical scores for use in an assembly or a church requires a licence. The following licences from Christian Copyright Licensing Limited (www.ccli.com) permit the photocopying or reproduction of song lyrics or musical scores – for example to create song sheets, overhead transparencies or to display the lyrics or music using any electronic display medium:

For UK schools: A Collective Worship Copyright Licence and a Music Reproduction Licence
For churches: A Church Copyright and Music Reproduction Licence

Please ensure that you log the songs that are used on your CCLI and MRL copy report.

Organisations that do not hold one of the above licences should contact Out of the Ark Limited directly for permission.

Your CCLI licence also grants you permission to display the song lyrics from our Words on Screen™ CD ROMS on a whiteboard or other screen. Simply log the song titles on your copy report.

Copying and File-sharing

Copying Out of the Ark Music's audio CDs is not permitted without obtaining a licence from the publisher. Installation of Out of the Ark Music's audio CD tracks on to a computer is strictly forbidden without a licence – we can provide schools with a 'Learning Platform Installation Licence'. File-sharing of any of our audio tracks or CD ROM files is strictly prohibited. For more information visit **www.outoftheark.com/licensing**.

Helpful information can be found on the following website:

A Guide to Licensing Copyright in Schools: www.outoftheark.com/licensing

And remember, we are always happy to help. For advice simply contact our customer services team:

Tel: +44 (0)20 8481 7200
Email: copyright@outoftheark.com

LICENCE APPLICATION FORM
(Prickly Hay)

If you perform **Prickly Hay** to an audience other than children and staff you will need to photocopy and complete this form and return it by post or fax to Out of the Ark Music in order to apply for a licence. If anticipated audience sizes are very small or if special circumstances apply please contact Out of the Ark Music.

The licence will permit the holder to:

- Perform *Prickly Hay* on the dates applied for.
- Reproduce the lyrics to the songs on printed paper, such as for programmes, and to make transparencies for overhead projection. The following credit should be included: *'Reproduced by kind permission © Out of the Ark Ltd'.*
- Photocopy the script for learning purposes. Copies must be destroyed after the performance.
- Make no more than two copies of the music, to be used by participating musicians on the performance dates.

If the performance is to be recorded please contact Out of the Ark Music.

We wish to apply for a licence to perform *Prickly Hay* by Mary Cliff and Kelly Fort

Customer number (if known): ....

Name of school / organisation: ....

Name of organiser / producer: ....

Date(s) of performance(s): ....

Invoice address: ....

....

Post code: .... **Country:** ....

Telephone number: ....

Number of performances (excl. dress rehearsal)	**Performances without admission charges**	**Performances with admission charges**
1	☐ **£14.40*** [€18.75]	☐ **£19.20** [€25.00]
2	☐ **£19.20** [€25.00]	☐ **£24.00** [€31.20]
3 or more	☐ **£24.00** [€31.20]	☐ **£30.13** [€39.20]

Tick one of the boxes above.

☐ Tick here to receive licensing information for any audio or video recording of a performance.

Tick one of the four payment options below: (Invoices will be sent with all licences)

☐ Please bill my school/nursery at the above address (UK schools/nurseries only)

☐ I enclose a cheque (Pounds Sterling) for £ .... payable to Out of the Ark Music

☐ I enclose a cheque (Euro) for € .... payable to Out of the Ark Music

☐ Please charge the following card: (Visa [not Electron], MasterCard & Maestro accepted)

Card No ....

Start Date _ _ / _ _ (MM/YY) Expiry Date _ _ / _ _ (MM/YY) 3 digit security code: _ _ _ (last 3 digits on signature strip)

Address: Out of the Ark Music
Kingsway Business Park
Oldfield Road
Hampton
Middlesex TW12 2HD
United Kingdom

Phone: +44 (0)20 8481 7200
Fax: +44 (0)20 8941 5548
Email: info@outoftheark.com

*The licence fees shown on this form are for 2011-2012 and include VAT at 20%. Prices may be subject to revision. Customers outside the EU will NOT be charged VAT.